STECK-VAUGHN/BERRENT

KEYS TO EXCELLENCE

in Integrated Language Arts

Susan C. Kramer, M.S.

STECK-VAUGHN
BERRENT
PUBLICATIONS

Keys to Excellence in Integrated Language Arts
Level F

ISBN # 0-8172-6253-9

Published by Steck-Vaughn/Berrent Publications, a division of Steck-Vaughn Publishing Corporation.

2 3 4 5 6 7 8 9   HG   01 00 99 98 97

Table of Contents

TO THE TEACHER

Keys to Excellence is a series of instructional books that includes a variety of genres of reading passages with higher order thinking questions. It introduces the **Get Ready-Read-ROAR** method. Students are presented with a step-by-step procedure that enables them to read selections, understand what they have read, and prepare and write answers to short- and extended-response questions.

To achieve excellence, students should follow the steps described before, during, and after they read the selection.

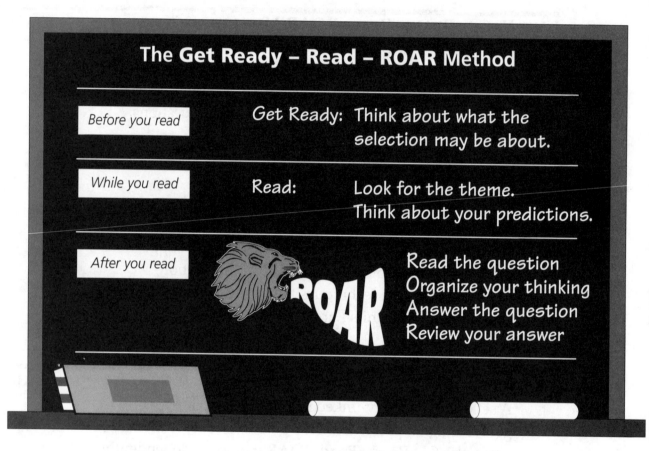

The **Get Ready – Read – ROAR** Method

| Before you read | Get Ready: | Think about what the selection may be about. |

| While you read | Read: | Look for the theme. Think about your predictions. |

| After you read | ROAR | Read the question
Organize your thinking
Answer the question
Review your answer |

When students see **Get Ready**, it is a clue for them to prepare to read. The next step is to **Read** the selection. After reading the selection, students utilize the **ROAR** method to answer questions.

Unit I

GRAPHIC ORGANIZERS

It is important to understand what you read. Graphic organizers can be used to help you recall and understand what you have read. Graphic organizers can also help you write about what you read. Graphic organizers will help you put your reading and thinking in order.

This section will teach you how to use different organizers.

SEQUENCE MAP

Sequence is the order in which events happen. A **Sequence Map** shows you the order of the events in a story.

Read the passage below. Then follow the directions.

Robots

Robots are very useful in today's modern world. Some people think that robots are a new idea. That is not true. For more than two thousand years, people have been trying to make machines that copy what living things do.

The first robot was made by a Greek inventor. He built a pigeon that looked real, though it was fake. Workers in France built a mechanical lion in the year 1500. It was able to walk around the court of the King. In the 1700s, a Swiss clockmaker built a puppet. It looked like a child sitting at a desk. The puppet seemed to have the intelligence of a thinking being. However, it needed assistance from a human being to make it work.

Many of these early robots were made just for fun. Now robots are very complicated machines with many different uses.

✏ Fill in the missing parts of this graphic organizer.

SEQUENCE MAP

FIRST:
The first robot was made by a Greek inventor.

↓

NEXT:
In the year 1500, a mechanical lion was built in France.

↓

NEXT: Swiss clockmaker built a Puppet.

↓

LAST: Many of these early robots were made just for fun.

✏ Now write a paragraph that tells about what you will do next week. First, make a Sequence Map. Then use the map to help you write the paragraph.

STORY MAP

A **Story Map** helps you to understand the parts of a story. Read the passage below. Then follow the directions.

Jackie Robinson

Crack! Bat meets ball and Dodgers' Jackie Robinson quickly runs to third base. Then he steals home, scoring a run.

Robinson was also great while playing second base. He was such an excellent fielder that he could catch even the most difficult balls hit to him.

In 1947, Robinson was named Rookie of the Year. In 1949, he won the National League's Most Valuable Player award. Each year he grew more popular. He was the first black man to play Major League Baseball. At that time, there was an unwritten rule that blacks could not play in the Major Leagues. Branch Rickey, the Brooklyn Dodgers' president, chose a very brave person to end this rule. Robinson was courageous enough to play while hearing terrible insults.

✎ Fill in the missing parts of this graphic organizer.

STORY MAP

CHARACTERS

1. Jackie Robinson
Branch Rickey
Jackie Robinson

SETTING

Where: Brooklyn

When: _1947 - 1949_

_____

STORY TITLE
The name of the story

Jackie Robinson

MOOD

1. amazement
2) _courageous_
3) _Brave_

_____

EVENTS

1. Jackie Robinson in Major Leagues
2) _Name Booleie of the year_

PROBLEM

Black men had been excluded from playing Major League Baseball.

SOLUTION

Jackie Robinson was courageous enough to still play while hearing terrible insults

✎ Now write a story that tells about a day that did not go very well. First, make a story map. Then use the map to help you write the story. Remember to include all the parts of the story map in the story you write.

VENN DIAGRAM

A **Venn Diagram** is a picture that shows in what ways two things are alike and not alike.

Read the passage below. Then follow the directions.

The Athletes

Two runners stand side by side at the starting line of a race. Both look very strong and fast. But one runner speeds ahead and wins the race. The other falls behind.

Everyone knows that athletes work out to strengthen their bodies. But research shows that strengthening the mind may be just as important. The best athletes win partly because they think they can win. Positive thoughts seem to give them an edge for success. They must create pictures in their minds of each move they must make in order to win. On the other hand, people who fail often think, "I can't win."

✎ Fill in the missing parts of this graphic organizer.

VENN DIAGRAM

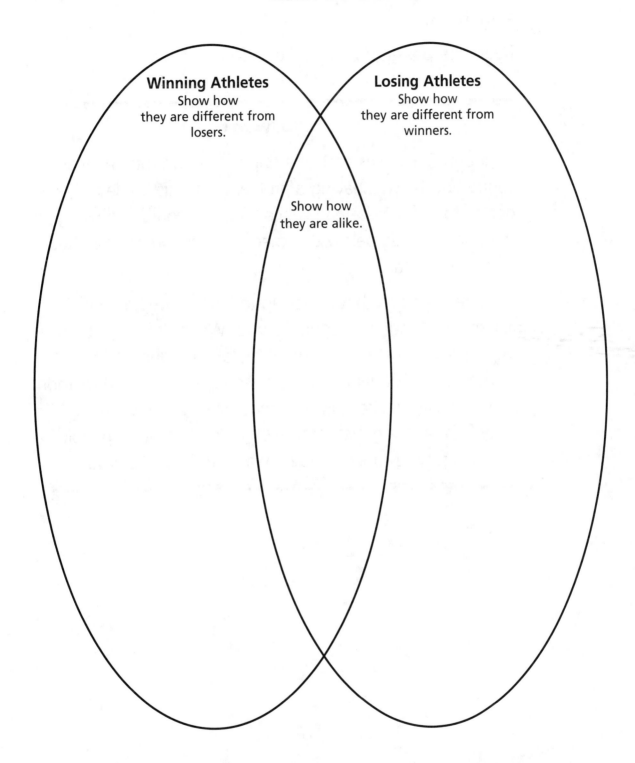

Winning Athletes
Show how
they are different from
losers.

Losing Athletes
Show how
they are different from
winners.

Show how
they are alike.

✎ Now write a story comparing two pets. Tell how they are alike and how they are different. First, make a Venn Diagram. Then use it to write the story.

DESCRIPTIVE MAP I

The **Descriptive Map** will help you describe someone or something.

Read the passage below. Then follow the directions.

Survivor

Robert Small was part of a happy family. When he was a young boy, he was having a problem with his left leg. The doctor found that he had cancer. Robert would need surgery to remove his leg below the knee. He was sad and terrified that he might die.

Robert realized that it was up to him to overcome his illness and decided he could survive. When Robert got a new leg, it was a prosthesis made of metal and rubber. He learned to walk again and practiced walking every day. Soon he was riding a bike, climbing mountains and swimming. Now that he is a grown man, he knows that other people can also survive cancer, and he wants to help them do it!

✎ Fill in the missing parts of this graphic organizer.

DESCRIPTIVE MAP I

brave

determined

ROBERT SMALL

An example that shows that Robert was brave is:

he worked to overcome his illness

Examples that show that Robert was determined are:

• he rode a bike

• he swam

An example

An example

An example

✎ Now write a story that describes a favorite relative. First, make a Descriptive Map like this one. Then use the map to help you write the story.

DESCRIPTIVE MAP II

The **Descriptive Map** will also help you describe two or more things.

Read the passage below. Then follow the directions.

Treasure Hunters

Over the years, many treasure hunters searched for the sunken ship Atocha. In 1972, Mel Fisher and Bob Holloway found the ship. It was not an easy task to search for undersea treasure. Through the years, the sea had wrecked the ship and buried the hull. The ship's body was under shifting sands. Fisher and Holloway used two boats in their search. They each took different equipment. Holloway's boat had magnets that could find metal far below the surface. When magnets showed evidence of metal, Holloway threw a buoy into the water so Fisher would know where to search. The second boat carried digging tools and diving gear so the divers could scuba dive to find the treasure.

✎ Fill in the missing parts of this graphic organizer.

DESCRIPTIVE MAP II

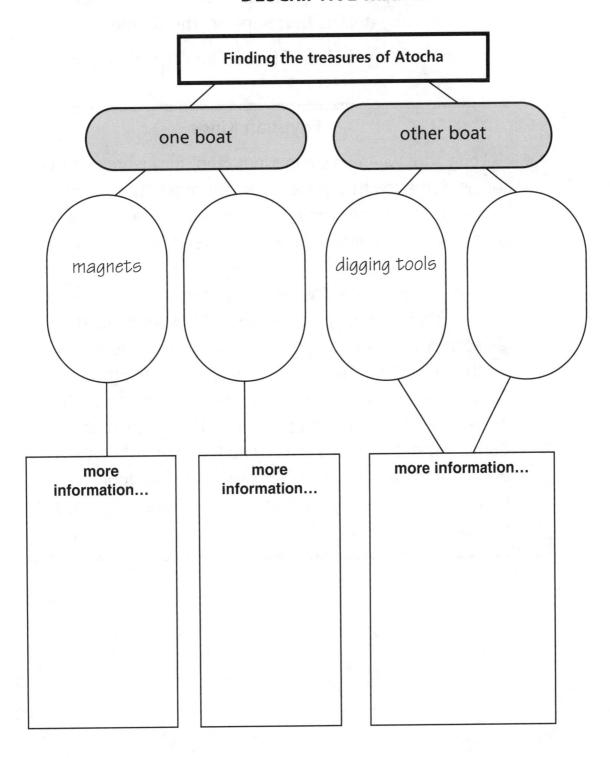

Finding the treasures of Atocha

one boat   other boat

magnets   digging tools

more information...   more information...   more information...

✎ Now write a passage about your favorite TV shows. First, make a Descriptive Map like this one. Then use the map to help you write the passage.

THEME MAP

A **Theme Map** shows the main topic or subject of a story. It also shows the details that support the theme.

Read the passage below. Then follow the directions.

Egyptian Kings

Long ago, when Egyptian Kings died, they were placed in tombs. Some tombs were as large as houses. They had chambers, or rooms, where the king and his treasures were buried. Archaeologists searched for these tombs. But all the graves found had been robbed long ago. However, the tomb of King Tutankhamen was still to be found. Howard Carter, a British archaeologist, was eager to find this tomb. Lord Carnarvon, a wealthy Englishman, gave Carter the money for the expedition. Carter and his team went to Egypt in 1922. His search led him to the entrance of an ancient tomb in the area of the Egyptian pyramids. He sent for Lord Carnarvon so they could investigate together. When they opened the tomb they were amazed. They had found what they had been seeking, the tomb of King Tutankhamen, still containing its riches.

✎ Fill in the missing parts of this graphic organizer.

THEME MAP

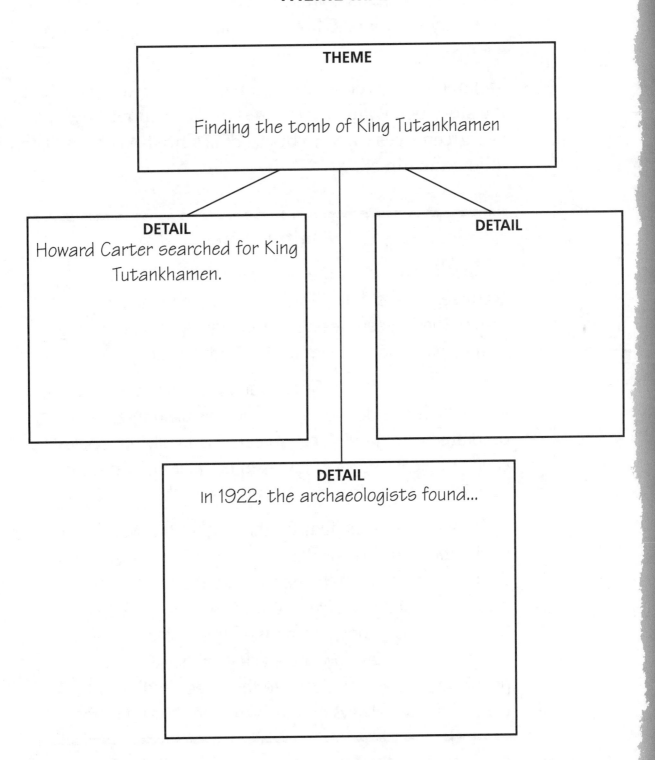

THEME

Finding the tomb of King Tutankhamen

DETAIL
Howard Carter searched for King Tutankhamen.

DETAIL

DETAIL
In 1922, the archaeologists found...

✎ Now write a paragraph about a trip you took or would like to take. Think about the theme and the details. Make a Theme Map. Then use the map to help you write the story.

CAUSE AND EFFECT MAP

A **Cause and Effect Map** shows what happens in a story and why it happens. It shows the relationship between events.

Melanie was given an assignment to write a fairy tale. In the story below, read the tale she wrote about how evergreen trees came to be used as Christmas trees. Then follow the directions.

Christmas Trees

Once upon a time, the Holly family thought that evergreens, trees that stayed green in the winter, were magic. These green trees made the family think of spring, so they put food on them for the birds to eat.

Their neighbors, the Serene family, decided to put a tree inside the house during the winter. This plain tree was decorated with good things to eat. The family put apples, candy, and cookies on it. It was to be their first Christmas tree. They also decided to put candles on the tree.

Through the years, families throughout the world have celebrated Christmas by decorating evergreen trees. Sometimes they use a theme to make their trees look a certain way. Some people put ribbons, toys, glass balls, bells, or chains of popcorn on their trees. Since candles can cause fires, families now use electric lights. Although people may choose to decorate their trees in different ways, there will always be the evergreen Christmas tree.

✎ Fill in the missing parts of this graphic organizer.

CAUSE AND EFFECT MAP

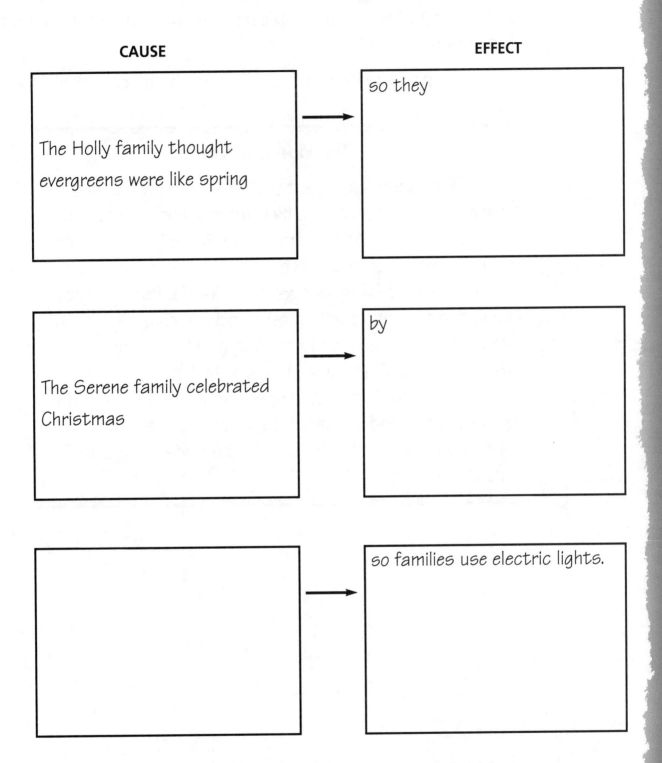

CAUSE

EFFECT

The Holly family thought evergreens were like spring

so they

The Serene family celebrated Christmas

by

so families use electric lights.

✎ Now write a passage in which you tell a child how to get good grades in school. First, make a Cause and Effect Map like this one. Then use the map to help you write the passage.

MAIN IDEA MAP

A **Main Idea Map** shows the most important idea and supporting ideas, or subtopics. It also has information about the subtopics.

Read the passage below. Then follow the directions.

The Monster Spider

You are trapped in a giant sticky net. A hairy monster appears and surrounds you. Its eight legs encircle you. This might sound like a bad dream to you. But it happens every night to millions of insects. The monster is a spider, and the net is its web. To us, spider webs are fragile. But the webs are strong enough to hold most insects. Because the webs are flexible, the spider can bend them to hold trapped insects in place. A spider spins a web by letting out liquid silk from its body. The liquid dries and forms a thread. The spider ties one end of the silk to a wall or a tree. Then it suspends itself from the thread. As the spider hangs, the thread gets longer.

✎ Fill in the missing parts of this graphic organizer.

MAIN IDEA MAP

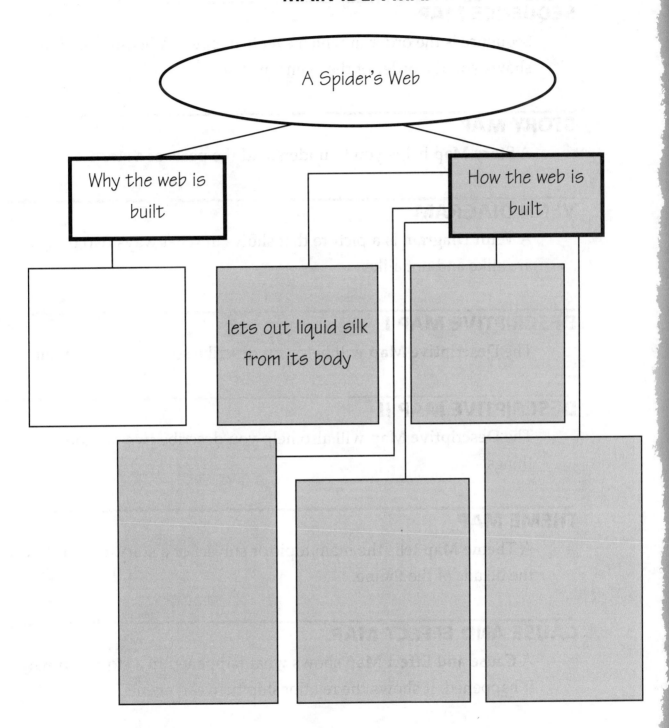

✎ Now write a story about a career you might choose. First, make a Main Idea Map like this one. Then use the map to help you write the story.

REVIEW OF GRAPHIC ORGANIZERS

SEQUENCE MAP

Sequence is the order in which events happen. A **Sequence Map** shows you the order of the events in a story.

STORY MAP

A **Story Map** helps you to understand the parts of a story.

VENN DIAGRAM

A **Venn Diagram** is a picture that shows in what ways two things are alike and not alike.

DESCRIPTIVE MAP I

The **Descriptive Map** will help you describe someone or something.

DESCRIPTIVE MAP II

The **Descriptive Map** will also help you describe two or more things.

THEME MAP

A **Theme Map** tells the main topic or subject of a story. It also shows the details of the theme.

CAUSE AND EFFECT MAP

A **Cause and Effect Map** shows what happened in a story and why it happened. It shows the relationship between events.

MAIN IDEA MAP

A **Main Idea Map** shows the most important idea and supporting ideas, or subtopics. It also has information about the subtopics.

GET READY – READ – ROAR METHOD

Now you know how to organize your thinking. Next you will learn how to read and understand what you read. We will show you the **Get Ready – Read – ROAR** method.

The **Get Ready – Read – ROAR** Method

Before you read	Get Ready:	Think about what the selection may be about.
While you read	Read:	Look for the theme. Think about your predictions.
After you read	**ROAR**	Read the question Organize your thinking Answer the question Review your answer.

SELECTION ONE: *From a Railway Carriage*

STEP 1: GET READY

First, you need to get ready to read. This is the time to think about what the selection may be about.

- **Read** the title.

- **Look** at the picture.

- Try to **guess** what the story may be about. This is called **making a prediction**.

You are about to read a poem. The title of this poem is *From a Railway Carriage*. It is written by Robert Louis Stevenson.

- Read the title and look at the picture on the next page.

- Try to guess what the poem may be about. This is called predicting what will happen.

What do you think this story could be about?

_____

_____

_____

_____

The theme of *From a Railway Carriage* is:
Traveling is an adventure.

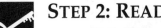

STEP 2: READ

While reading the poem, think about the theme, **traveling is an adventure**. Think about your predictions.

From a Railway Carriage
by Robert Louis Stevenson

Faster than fairies, faster than witches,
Bridges and houses, hedges and ditches;
And charging along like troops in a battle,
All through the meadows the horses and cattle,

All of the sights of the hill and the plain
Fly as thick as driving rain;
And ever again, in the wink of an eye,
Painted stations whistle by.

Here is a child who clambers and scrambles,
All by himself and gathering brambles;
Here is a tramp who stands and gazes;
And there is the green for stringing the daisies!

Here is a cart run away in the road
Lumping along with man and load;
And here is a mill and there is a river,
Each a glimpse and gone for ever!

STEP 3:

Now you are ready to answer some questions about this poem. To do this, you will use **ROAR**.

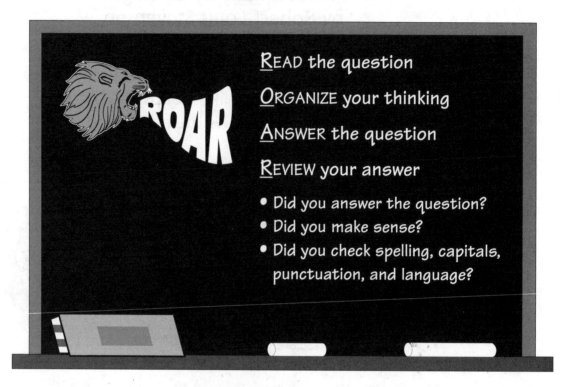

<u>R</u>EAD the question

<u>O</u>RGANIZE your thinking

<u>A</u>NSWER the question

<u>R</u>EVIEW your answer
- Did you answer the question?
- Did you make sense?
- Did you check spelling, capitals, punctuation, and language?

So **ROAR** means
<u>R</u>EAD, <u>O</u>RGANIZE, <u>A</u>NSWER, <u>R</u>EVIEW

Use **ROAR** *to answer the following question:*

1. What are the main parts of this poem?
   Complete the story map to show the main parts.

■ **ROAR** — <u>R</u>EAD the question

What does the question ask you to do? _____

_____

■ ROAR — **O**RGANIZE your thinking

Think about the characters, setting, events, and mood of the story.

■ ROAR — **A**NSWER the question

Complete the story map below.

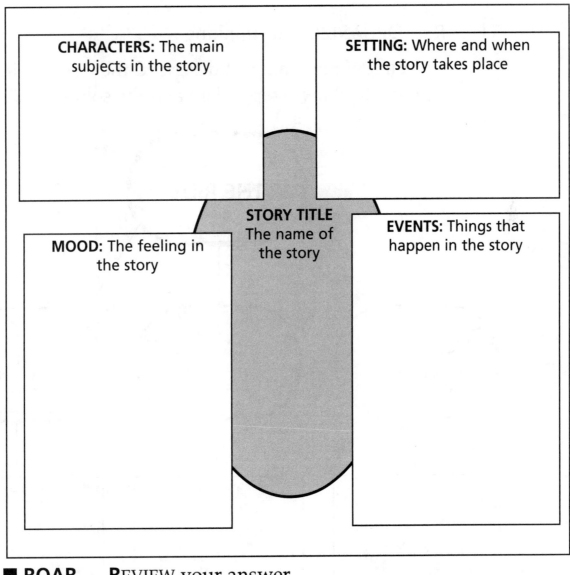

CHARACTERS: The main subjects in the story

SETTING: Where and when the story takes place

STORY TITLE The name of the story

MOOD: The feeling in the story

EVENTS: Things that happen in the story

■ ROAR — **R**EVIEW your answer

- Did you answer the question? ❏ yes ❏ no
- Did you make sense? ❏ yes ❏ no
- Did you check spelling, capitals, punctuation, language? ❏ yes ❏ no

2. How does the poet describe the train ride?

■ **ROAR** — **R**EAD the question

What does the question ask you to do? _____

_____

■ **R**O**AR** — **O**RGANIZE your thinking

Think of how the poet described the ride. Fill in the chart to show the problem and the solution.

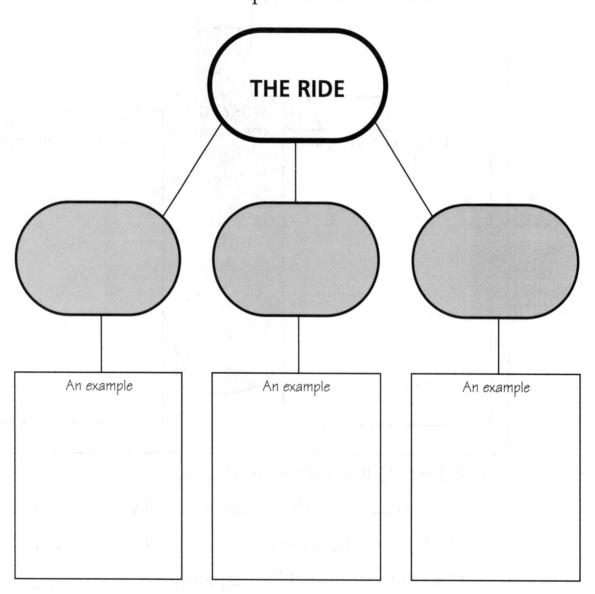

■ ROAR — **A**NSWER the question

_____

_____

_____

_____

_____

_____

_____

_____

_____

_____

_____

_____

_____

_____

_____

_____

_____

■ ROAR — **R**EVIEW your answer

- Did you answer the question?   ❏ yes   ❏ no

- Did you make sense?   ❏ yes   ❏ no

- Did you check spelling, capitals,
  punctuation, language?   ❏ yes   ❏ no

3. How do you think the poet feels about the train ride?

■ **R**OAR — **R**EAD the question

What does the question ask you to do? _____

_____

■ **R**O**A**R — **O**RGANIZE your thinking

> Look back at the poem to see how the poet feels about the train ride.
>
> | The poet feels... | |
> |---|---|
> | | |

■ **R**O**A**R — **A**NSWER the question

Write about how the poet feels in this poem. Remember to give examples from the poem.

_____

_____

_____

_____

_____

_____

■ **R**OA**R** — **R**EVIEW your answer

- •Did you answer the question?   ❑ yes   ❑ no

- •Did you make sense?   ❑ yes   ❑ no

- •Did you check spelling, capitals,
  punctuation, language?   ❑ yes   ❑ no

SELECTION TWO: *One Summer Vacation*

You are going to read another selection. It has the same theme as *From a Railway Carriage*. This selection is a story. It is called *One Summer Vacation*.

STEP 1: GET READY

Remember, this is the time to think about what the selection may be about.

- **Read** the title on the next page.

- **Look** at the picture on the next page.

- Try to **guess** what the story may be about. This is called **making a prediction**.

- What do you think this story could be about?

_____

_____

- Do you remember the theme of the poem *From a Railway Carriage*? The theme of the poem was _____

_____

This story has the same theme as *From A Railway Carriage*.

- Now what do you think the story may be about?

_____

_____

STEP 2: READ

Read the story. Look for the theme. See if your predictions were correct. Remember the theme is **traveling is an adventure.**

One Summer Vacation

Every day was hot and beautiful. I took my boat down to the river quite a bit. Each time I went to the same spot, hoping that someone would be there so that I would have some company. Soon I became very good friends with David, who was on the river all the time.

One day David suggested we take a trip down the river on a raft. It sounded so exciting that I could hardly wait. We borrowed his father's raft and went for a ride.

The raft was not too big. It was made out of wooden planks and was in great condition. We each had a pole to help guide us down the river. It was about ten o'clock when we began our journey.

Once we were on the river, we saw huge steamboats gliding passed us. The shore was lined with giant mansions. These large old white houses looked like typical southern plantations.

We tried to stay close to the river bank so that we could control the raft more easily. As we traveled, we saw factories and old battlefields. I thought of all the historic battles that must have been fought here. Soon we decided to stop and have a picnic lunch in a quiet inlet. We tried to tie the raft onto a huge wooden log near one of the fields but we had some difficulty. Finally, an older gentleman appeared and asked if he could assist us. Soon we were anchored to the log. This was one adventure I would never forget!

You are going to be asked some questions about the story you just read. Use ROAR to answer them.

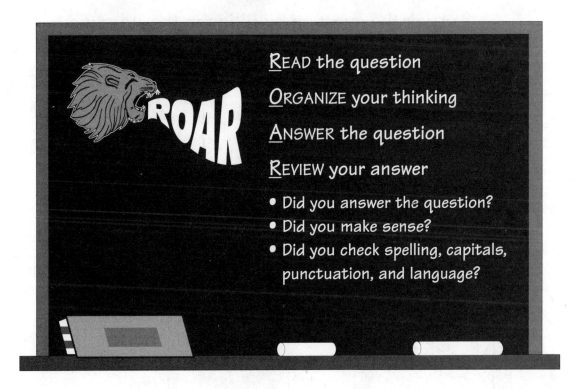

READ the question

ORGANIZE your thinking

ANSWER the question

REVIEW your answer

• Did you answer the question?
• Did you make sense?
• Did you check spelling, capitals, punctuation, and language?

So **ROAR** means
READ, ORGANIZE, ANSWER, REVIEW

---

4. What are the main parts of this story? Complete the story map on the next page.

■ **ROAR** — READ the question

What does the question ask you to do? _____

_____

■ **ROAR** — ORGANIZE your thinking

Think about:

• Who are the characters?

• What are the key events?

- Where does the story take place? When does the story take place?
- What is the mood of the story?

■ RO**A**R — **A**NSWER the question

Answer the question by filling in the story map.

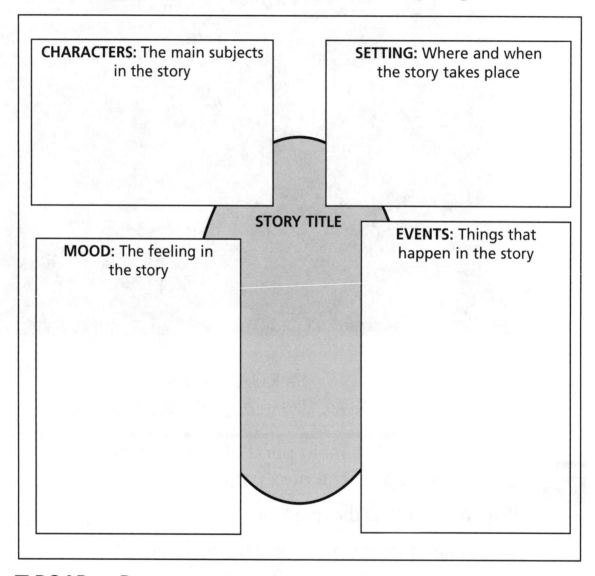

CHARACTERS: The main subjects in the story

SETTING: Where and when the story takes place

STORY TITLE

MOOD: The feeling in the story

EVENTS: Things that happen in the story

■ ROA**R** — **R**EVIEW your answer

- Did you answer the question?   ❏ yes   ❏ no
- Did you make sense?   ❏ yes   ❏ no
- Did you check spelling, capitals, punctuation, language?   ❏ yes   ❏ no

5. How does the narrator describe the summer adventure on the raft?

■ **ROAR** — **R**EAD the question

What does the question ask you to do? _____

_____

■ **RO**AR — **O**RGANIZE your thinking

Think about how the narrator described the trip down the river on a raft. Fill in the chart below.

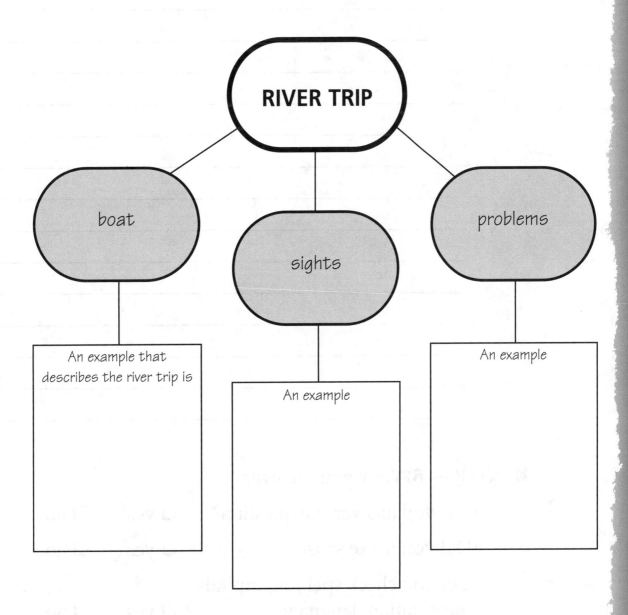

■ ROAR — **A**NSWER the question

Use the organizer to write a paragraph. _____

_____

_____

_____

_____

_____

_____

_____

_____

_____

_____

_____

_____

_____

_____

_____

_____

_____

_____

■ ROAR — **R**EVIEW your answer

- •Did you answer the question?   ❏ yes   ❏ no

- •Did you make sense?   ❏ yes   ❏ no

- •Did you check spelling, capitals,
  punctuation, language?   ❏ yes   ❏ no

Directions: This next question asks you to write about both selections. You must think about *From a Railway Carriage* and *One Summer Vacation.*

6. How do you think the narrator of the poem and the boy in the story compare? Write at least two paragraphs and give examples from the selections to explain your answer.

■ **R**OAR — **R**EAD the question

What does the question ask you to do? _____

_____

■ **R**O**A**R — **O**RGANIZE your thinking

Complete the Venn Diagram below.

• In the center section list things that are true for both the narrator of the poem and the boy in the story. In the other sections, list things that are true for each one individually.

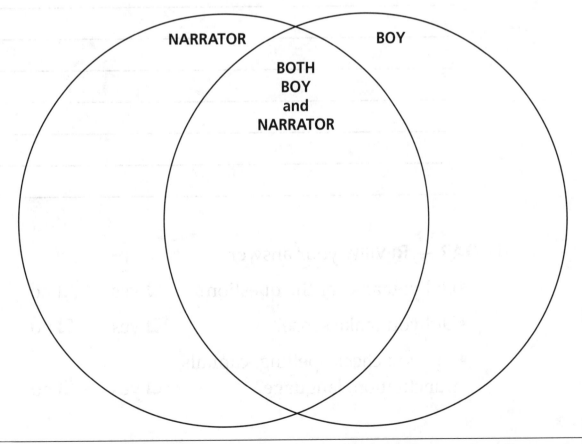

■ ROAR — **A**NSWER the question

Write two paragraphs that show the similarities and differences of the main characters. Use your organizer to help you answer the question.

- Tell how the narrator in the poem and the boy in the story are **alike** in your first paragraph.

- Tell how the narrator in the poem and the boy in the story are **different** in your second paragraph.

_____

_____

_____

_____

_____

_____

_____

_____

_____

_____

_____

_____

_____

_____

■ ROAR — **R**EVIEW your answer

- Did you answer the question? ❏ yes ❏ no

- Did you make sense? ❏ yes ❏ no

- Did you check spelling, capitals, punctuation, language? ❏ yes ❏ no

Unit III

GUIDED PRACTICE

In this unit you are going to read several selections. Each pair of selections is connected by a theme. You will be asked to answer questions about what you have read.

SECTION A   A tale: *Cap o' Rushes*

A poem: *The Village Blacksmith*

The first selection is an English tale about a girl, Cap o' Rushes. The second selection is a poem about a blacksmith who works hard. Both of the selections are based on the same theme.

The theme of the two selections is *hard work*.

✎ Write some of the things you know about this theme.

Hard work you did	Result of your hard work
1. _____	1. _____
_____	_____
_____	_____
2. _____	2. _____
_____	_____
_____	_____
3. _____	3. _____
_____	_____
_____	_____

SELECTION ONE: *Cap o' Rushes*

GET READY

• **READ THE TITLE**   • **LOOK AT THE PICTURES**   • **MAKE A PREDICTION**

This selection is about a girl, Cap o' Rushes. The theme of the story is *hard work*.

✎ Read the title and look at the pictures. Predict what *Cap o' Rushes* may be about.

_____

_____

_____

_____

_____

_____

_____

_____

_____

_____

READ

• **LOOK FOR THE THEME**   • **SEE IF YOU PREDICTED CORRECTLY**

In this part, you are going to read a tale called *Cap o' Rushes* written by an unknown author.

You will be asked to answer some questions about what you have read. Read and answer each question carefully. You can look back at the story as often as you like.

Cap o' Rushes

 There was once an extremely rich man, who had three daughters. He thought he'd see how much they loved him, so he asked the first, "How much do you love me, my dear?"

"I love you as I love my life," she replied.

"That's wonderful," he answered.

Then he turned to the second daughter, "How much do you love me, my dear?"

"Why," she answered, "better than anyone in all the world."

"That's wonderful," he replied.

Finally, he turned to the third daughter, "How much do you love me, my dear?"

"Why, I love you as fresh meat loves salt," she answered.

He was extremely angry and yelled out, "You don't love me at all, therefore you won't stay in my house." So he drove her out, and shut the door in her face.

She traveled very far until she discovered a marsh. There she gathered a lot of rushes and made them into a kind of a cloak with a hood, to cover herself from head to foot, and to hide her fine clothes. When she was done, she went on until she came to a mansion.

"Do you want a maid?" she asked.

"No, we don't," they replied.

"I have nowhere to go, and I ask no wages. I do any sort of work," she begged.

"Well, if you like to wash the pots and scrape the saucepans you may stay." Because she gave no name they called her "Cap o' Rushes."

One day there was to be a great dance a little way off. Cap o' Rushes relayed that she was too tired to go, and stayed at home. However, when everyone had gone, she took off her cap o' rushes, cleaned herself, and went to the dance. She was the best dressed person at the dance. Her master's son fell in love with her the minute he set eyes on her. He would dance with no one else and presented her with a most beautiful ring.

Before the dance was done, Cap o' Rushes slipped away and went home. When the other maids came back, she pretended to be asleep. The next morning they spoke to her about the dance. "You did miss a sight, Cap o' Rushes! The most beautiful lady was at the dance, and the young master never took his eyes off her."

"Well, I would like to have seen her," said Cap o' Rushes.

The master's son tried in every way to find out where the lady had gone. But he never heard anything about her, and he became sicker with each passing day until he had to take to his bed. The cook was ordered to make gruel for the young master. So she set about making it. Cap o' Rushes wandered into the kitchen, and upon seeing the cook, stated that she would make the master's gruel. When she had made it, she slipped the ring into it secretly before the cook took it upstairs.

The young man ate it, and when he saw the ring at the bottom, he demanded to see the cook. "Who made this gruel?" he shouted.

"Cap o' Rushes," she stammered.

"Send her in to see me immediately!" he screamed. So Cap o' Rushes came in to see the master. "Did you make my gruel?" he demanded.

"Yes, I did," she replied. "Where did you get this ring?" he inquired. "From you, sir, " she said shyly. "Who are you, then?" asked the young man. "I'll show you," she said. And she took off her cap o' rushes, and there she was in her beautiful clothes.

They were married within a short period of time. It was a very grand wedding, and every one was asked from far and near, even Cap o' Rushes' father was invited. But she had never told anybody who she was.

Before the wedding, Cap o' Rushes went to the cook and said, "I want you to prepare every dish without any salt."

"Very well," the cook replied.

After the wedding, all of the company sat down to the dinner. When they began to eat the meat, it was so tasteless they couldn't eat it. Cap o' Rushes' father tried first one dish and then another, and then he burst out crying.

"What is the matter?" the master's son said to him.

"Oh!" said the father. "I had a daughter. When I asked her how much she loved me, she said 'As much as fresh meat loves salt.' I turned her from my door, for I thought she didn't love me. Now I see she loved me best of all. She may be dead for all I know."

"No, Father, here she is!" said Cap o' Rushes. She went up to him, put her arms around him and embraced him. They all lived happily ever after.

Directions: Answer the following questions about Cap o' Rushes. Look back at the story as often as you like.

---

1. Complete the chart on the next page showing some of the important parts of this story.

■ **ROAR** — **R**EAD the question

What does the question ask you to do? _____

_____

■ **R<u>O</u>AR** — **O**RGANIZE your thinking

- Characters
  Who was the main character? or Who were the main characters?

- Setting
  Where did the story take place? When did the story take place?

- Mood
  The feeling in the story

- Events
  Things that happened in the story

- Problem
  What was the conflict in the story?

- Solution
  How was it resolved?

■ ROAR — **A**NSWER the question

Use the organizer to help you write your answer. Choose what you think are the most important acts.

CHARACTERS

1. Cap o' Rushes

_____

_____

_____

SETTING

Where: the countryside

_____

When: _____

STORY TITLE

Cap o' Rushes

PROBLEM

Cap o' Rushes' father sent her away.

SOLUTION

_____
_____
_____
_____
_____
_____
_____
_____
_____
_____
_____

■ ROAR — **R**EVIEW your answer

- •Did you answer the question? ❑ yes ❑ no

- •Did you make sense? ❑ yes ❑ no

- •Did you check spelling, capitals, punctuation, language? ❑ yes ❑ no

2. What character traits can you use to best describe Cap o' Rushes? Complete the chart on the next page.

■ **ROAR** — **R**EAD the question

What does the question ask you to do? _____

_____

■ **ROAR** — **O**RGANIZE your thinking

Think of words that describe Cap o' Rushes. Complete this list first to help you organize your thinking.

What words or phrases best describe Cap o' Rushes? What examples can you use to support your descriptive words?

word or phrases	example from story

■ ROAR — **A**NSWER the question

Which are the **two best** words or phrases that you used in your organizer to describe Cap o' Rushes? Complete the chart using these words.

CAP O' RUSHES

A word or phrase that best describes Cap o' Rushes is...

A word or phrase that best describes Cap o' Rushes is...

Support from the story...

_____

_____

_____

_____

_____

_____

_____

Support from the story...

_____

_____

_____

_____

_____

_____

_____

■ ROAR — **R**EVIEW your answer

- Did you answer the question?   ❏ yes   ❏ no

- Did you make sense?   ❏ yes   ❏ no

- Did you check spelling, capitals, punctuation, language?   ❏ yes   ❏ no

3. Discuss the lesson learned by Cap o' Rushes' father.

■ **ROAR — R**EAD the question

What does the question ask you to do? _____

_____

■ **RO**A**R — O**RGANIZE your thinking

How did Cap o' Rushes teach a lesson to her father?

THINGS CAP O' RUSHES DID	HOW HER FATHER REACTED

■ RO**A**R — **A**NSWER the question

Use the information in your organizer to write about the lesson Cap o' Rushes' father learned. Write three paragraphs. Be sure to describe what happened in the story.

_____

_____

_____

_____

_____

_____

_____

_____

_____

_____

_____

_____

_____

_____

_____

_____

_____

■ RO**A**R — **R**EVIEW your answer

- •Did you answer the question?   ❏ yes   ❏ no

- •Did you make sense?   ❏ yes   ❏ no

- •Did you check spelling, capitals, punctuation, language?   ❏ yes   ❏ no

SELECTION TWO: *The Village Blacksmith*

GET READY

- **READ THE TITLE** • **LOOK AT THE PICTURE** • **MAKE A PREDICTION**

The second selection is a poem about a blacksmith. It is called *The Village Blacksmith*. It was written by Henry Wadsworth Longfellow.

Read the poem. Answer the questions after the poem.

The theme of this poem is the same as the theme of the story, *Cap o' Rushes*. If you don't remember the theme, look back at the beginning of this section.

✎ What is the theme?_____

_____

✎ What do you think will happen in this poem? Make your predictions.

1. _____

_____

_____

2. _____

_____

_____

READ

- **LOOK FOR THE THEME** • **SEE IF YOU PREDICTED CORRECTLY**

Read the poem to look for the theme and see if you predicted correctly.

The Village Blacksmith
by Henry Wadsworth Longfellow

Under a spreading chestnut-tree
The village smithy stands;
The smith, a mighty man is he,
With large and sinewy hands;
And the muscles of his brawny arms
Are strong as iron bands.

His hair is crisp, and black, and long,
His face is like the tan;
His brow is wet with honest sweat,
He earns whate'er he can,
And looks the whole world in the face,
For he owes not any man.

Week in, week out, from morn till night,
You can hear his bellows blow;
You can hear him swing his heavy sledge,
With measured beat and slow,
Like a sexton ringing the village bell,
When the evening sun is low.

And children coming home from school
Look in at the open door;
They love to see the flaming forge,
And hear the bellows roar,
And catch the burning sparks that fly
Like chaff from a threshing floor.

He goes on Sunday to the church,
And sits among his boys;
He hears the parson pray and preach,
He hears his daughter's voice
Singing in the village choir,
And it makes his heart rejoice.

It sounds to him like her mother's voice,
Singing in Paradise!

He needs must think of her once more,
How in the grave she lies;
And with his hard, rough hand he wipes
A tear out of his eyes.

Toiling, rejoicing, sorrowing,
Onward through life he goes;
Each morning sees some task begin,
Each evening sees it close;
Something attempted, something done,
Has earned a night's repose.

Thanks, thanks to thee, my worthy friend,
For the lesson thou hast taught!
Thus at the flaming forge of life
Our Fortunes must be wrought;
Thus on its sounding anvil shaped
Each burning deed and thought!

Directions: Answer questions 4 through 6. You may look back at the poem as often as you like.

4. Write at least two paragraphs to describe the village blacksmith.

■ **ROAR** — **R**EAD the question

What does the question ask? _____

_____

■ **ROAR** — **O**RGANIZE your thinking

What words or phrases best describe the village blacksmith? What examples can you use to explain your descriptive words?

WORD OR PHRASE	SUPPORT FROM STORY
very strong	you could hear him swing his heavy sledge

■ ROAR — **A**NSWER the question

Use the information in your organizer to write at least two paragraphs to describe the village blacksmith.

_____

_____

_____

_____

_____

_____

_____

_____

_____

_____

_____

_____

_____

_____

_____

_____

_____

_____

_____

■ ROAR — **R**EVIEW your answer

- Did you answer the question?   ❏ yes   ❏ no

- Did you make sense?   ❏ yes   ❏ no

- Did you check spelling, capitals,
  punctuation, language?   ❏ yes   ❏ no

5. What is the lesson referred to in the last stanza of the poem?

■ R̲OAR — R̲EAD the question

What does the question ask? _____

_____

■ RO̲AR — O̲RGANIZE your thinking

> Reread the last stanza.
>
> What is the lesson the narrator mentions? Think about how the poet describes the blacksmith.

■ ROA̲R — A̲NSWER the question

_____

_____

_____

_____

_____

_____

_____

_____

_____

_____

_____

_____

_____

■ ROAR̲ — R̲EVIEW your answer

- •Did you answer the question?   ❑ yes   ❑ no

- •Did you make sense?   ❑ yes   ❑ no

- •Did you check spelling, capitals, punctuation, language?   ❑ yes   ❑ no

Directions: This question is about both selections.

6. The main characters in the two selections work hard. Compare the results of their hard work.

■ **ROAR** — **R**EAD the question

What does the question ask? _____

_____

■ **R**O**AR** — **O**RGANIZE your thinking

Compare the work of the main characters in the two selections.

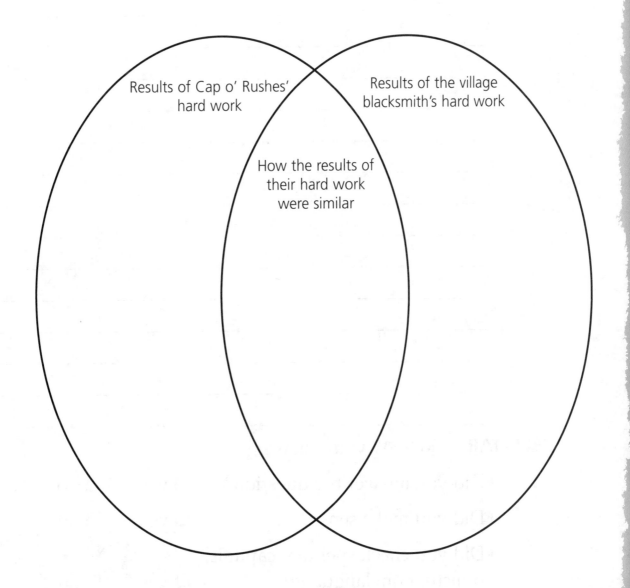

Results of Cap o' Rushes' hard work

Results of the village blacksmith's hard work

How the results of their hard work were similar

■ ROAR — **A**NSWER the question

Write two paragraphs that answer the question. Remember to look for similarities and differences between the main characters and their hard work.

_____

_____

_____

_____

_____

_____

_____

_____

_____

_____

_____

_____

_____

_____

_____

_____

_____

_____

_____

_____

_____

■ ROAR — **R**EVIEW your answer

- •Did you answer the question?   ❏ yes   ❏ no

- •Did you make sense?   ❏ yes   ❏ no

- •Did you check spelling, capitals, punctuation, language?   ❏ yes   ❏ no

SECTION B   Story 1: *Solo Voyage*

Story 2: *Golda Meir*

In this section you are going to read two stories. You will then be asked to answer some questions about them.

The first selection is a story about a man who takes a boat trip. The second selection is a story about Golda Meir. She was Israel's Prime Minister.

The theme connecting the two selections is *setting goals*.

Complete this chart. Write some goals you have set for yourself.

Goals you have...

_____

_____

_____

_____

_____

_____

_____

_____

SELECTION ONE: *Solo Voyage*

GET READY

- **READ THE TITLE**   • **LOOK AT THE PICTURES**   • **MAKE A PREDICTION**

✎ Read the title and look at the pictures. Predict what *Solo Voyage* may be about.

_____

_____

_____

_____

_____

_____

_____

_____

_____

READ

- **LOOK FOR THE THEME**   • **SEE IF YOU PREDICTED CORRECTLY**

In this part you are going to read a story called *Solo Voyage* by Ann Weil.

You will be asked to answer some questions about what you have read. Read each question carefully and do as it asks. You can look back at the story as often as you like.

Solo Voyage
by Ann Weil

Sailing around the world by himself turned out to be an adventure and a half for Bill Pinkney. Some of his experiences were definitely tough stuff!

For instance, south of Bermuda, Pinkney's sailboat, *The Commitment*, was boxed in by two hurricanes.

Then, there was the time he was caught in a lightning storm. *The Commitment* was the tallest thing around–perfect for attracting all that dangerous lightning. Luckily, the boat wasn't hit.

Was he afraid? You bet he was! But the 56-year-old Chicago resident put his fear to good use. "Experience and judgment got me through."

Bill Pinkney's solo voyage began on August 9, 1990, when he sailed south from Boston Harbor to Bermuda. Twenty-two months later, he became the fourth American and the first African-American to circle the globe "the hard way." He passed under the five southern capes, taking no short cuts through the Panama or Suez canals.

Although *The Commitment* was designed to sail with a crew of seven people,

the boat was rigged so that Pinkney could sail it alone. He used a series of special controls.

When he wasn't working to stay afloat, Pinkney read books and listened to music. Or he slept. Six hours of sleep a night was his usual limit. Sailing alone means you're always the one on duty. Some days, Pinkney could only rest a few hours because he had to keep watch for other large ships around him.

It took him 34 days to cross the Atlantic from Brazil to Cape Town, South Africa. That was an emotional arrival for him, "coming upon the continent of my ancestors."

Pinkney then struggled through the Indian Ocean to Tasmania. At times there were forty-foot waves and gale force winds. *The Commitment* was knocked over twice!

Pinkney arrived in Tasmania in April 1991. Conditions in the southern Pacific Ocean were too dangerous for him to continue just then. He decided to take a break. He flew home to see his wife and visit classrooms in Boston and Chicago.

Pinkney then returned to Tasmania. From there, he continued his journey. He met a fierce storm on his way to Stewart Island, south of New Zealand. Pinkney was out of radio contact for 72 hours. His friends and family were very worried. But he was all right—just a bit shaken from being bounced around.

After Tasmania, Pinkney faced what he called the "Big Daddy." Sailing around Cape Horn at the tip of South America was the longest single leg of his trip. He traveled nonstop for 64 days.

On June 9, 1992, Bill Pinkney sailed into Boston Harbor. He was greeted by the excited shouts of schoolchildren, friends, and family.

Pinkney considers himself a perfect example of the saying, "If you put your mind to something it can be done."

"There's no excuse for not making your dream come true," he says. "All you have to do is be willing to pay the price and work at it. Whether you're female or black—or anything—you can't let anybody else set your goals for you."

The Commitment is more than just the name of Pinkney's sailboat. It is his motto and his message: "You have to plan. You have to stick to it. Once you have made a commitment, you don't give it up, no matter what."

Bill Pinkney will never forget his great sailing adventure. And history won't forget him! The American flag Pinkney flew in every port is on permanent display at the DuSable Museum of African-American History in Chicago.

Directions: Answer questions 1 through 3 about *Solo Voyage*. Look back at the story as often as you like.

1.   Describe the main parts of Bill Pinkney's voyage. Write at least three paragraphs and use examples from the story.

■ ROAR — READ the question

What does the question ask? _____

_____

■ ROAR — ORGANIZE your thinking

What do you think are the parts of the voyage?

■ ROAR — **A**NSWER the question

Use the organizer to help you write your answer. Choose what you think are the most important events.

_____

_____

_____

_____

_____

_____

_____

_____

_____

_____

_____

_____

_____

■ ROAR — **R**EVIEW your answer

- Did you answer the question? ❑ yes ❑ no

- Did you make sense? ❑ yes ❑ no

- Did you check spelling, capitals, punctuation, language? ❑ yes ❑ no

2. How would you describe Bill Pinkney? Complete the chart on the next page.

■ **R**OAR — **R**EAD the question

What does the question ask? _____

_____

■ **RO**AR — **O**RGANIZE your thinking

What words or phrases best describe Bill Pinkney? What examples can you use to explain your descriptive words?

word or phrase	example from story
Loner	Made solo trip

■ ROAR — **A**NSWER the question

Select the two words or phrases that you used in your organizer that best describe Pinkney. Complete the chart using the space provided to extend your examples.

Bill Pinkney

A word or phrase that describes Pinkney is...

A word or phrase that describes Pinkney is...

An example...

_____
_____
_____
_____
_____
_____
_____
_____
_____

An example...

_____
_____
_____
_____
_____
_____
_____
_____
_____

■ ROAR — **R**EVIEW your answer

- •Did you answer the question? ❏ yes ❏ no
- •Did you make sense? ❏ yes ❏ no
- •Did you check spelling, capitals, punctuation, language? ❏ yes ❏ no

3. Assume you are a newspaper reporter. How would you describe Bill Pinkney's voyage?

■ **R**OAR — **R**EAD the question

What does the question ask? _____

_____

■ **RO**AR — **O**RGANIZE your thinking

What are the key events of Bill Pinkney's voyage?

FIRST:

↓

NEXT:

↓

NEXT:

↓

LAST:

■ ROAR — **A**NSWER the question

Be sure to use a good headline to catch the reader's attention. Using your organizer, describe the events. Write at least two paragraphs for your article.

THE HEADLINE: _____

_____

_____

_____

_____

_____

_____

_____

_____

_____

_____

_____

_____

_____

_____

_____

_____

_____

■ ROAR — **R**EVIEW your answer

- •Did you answer the question? ❑ yes ❑ no

- •Did you make sense? ❑ yes ❑ no

- •Did you check spelling, capitals, punctuation, language? ❑ yes ❑ no

SELECTION TWO: *Golda Meir*

GET READY

• **READ THE TITLE** • **LOOK AT THE PICTURE** • **MAKE A PREDICTION**

The second selection is a story called *Golda Meir* by Henry Billings and Melissa Stone. Read the story, then answer some questions about what you have read.

Do you remember the theme of these selections? If you don't remember, look back at the beginning of this section.

✎ What is the theme?

_____

_____

_____

✎ Read the title and look at the picture. Predict what *Golda Meir* may be about.

_____

_____

_____

_____

_____

_____

_____

READ

• **LOOK FOR THE THEME** • **SEE IF YOU PREDICTED CORRECTLY**

Read the story. Look for the theme. See if you predicted correctly.

Golda Meir
by Henry Billings and Melissa Stone

Four-year-old Golda Mabovitz sat on the stairs of her family's home in Kiev, Russia. She watched her father rushing to board up the windows and doors. Golda didn't understand exactly what was in danger. People in Kiev were planning a pogrom, or attack against the Jews. Because Golda's family was Jewish, they might be attacked. Any minute people might break into their home. These people might set the house on fire. They might rob, beat, or even kill Golda's family.

The pogrom planned for that day in 1902 never took place. Still, Golda never forgot the fear she felt while watching her father board up the windows. "It's not fair," she thought as she grew older. "We're peaceful people. We shouldn't be attacked just because our beliefs are different from those of other people."

Many Jews agreed with Golda. They felt Jews would never be safe until they had their own country. Golda and other Jews dreamed of living in Palestine, an area in the Middle East. This was the old Jewish homeland. For years the British had ruled Palestine. Many Arabs also lived there. But Golda hoped that someday this land would again belong to the Jews.

In 1921, Golda made a bold move. She decided she and her husband should live in Palestine. They could help create a Jewish state there. In Palestine, Golda went to work for the World Zionist Congress and the Jewish Agency for Palestine. She did all she could to make people see that Jews needed their own country.

During these years, Golda also struggled to raise a family. She had little money. Sometimes she took in washing. Often she could hardly afford to feed her children. She believed that Jews would never be safe until they had a home of their own.

In 1946, Golda became the head of the Jewish Agency. The following year, her wish came true. The United Nations agreed to turn Palestine into two countries. One would be an Arab state. The other would be the Jewish state of Israel.

Jews around the world celebrated when they heard the news. Golda, too, was happy. But she was also worried. She knew that Arabs didn't want half of Palestine. They wanted it all. She feared they would go to war to destroy Israel.

Golda did all she could to keep this war from happening. She gave a speech to the people of Palestine, asking them to honor the United Nations' vote.

But there would be no peace in Palestine. On November 29, 1947, fighting broke out. Arabs burned Jewish stores. They attacked Jewish buses. Arabs in neighboring countries got their armies ready to attack. "If we want to keep our country, we will have to fight for it," thought Golda.

Golda knew the Jews had little chance of winning a war. Arab armies had plenty of guns. They had airplanes and tanks. The Jews had no real army. They needed guns. But to buy guns, they needed money.

Golda decided she would try to get the money. Quickly, she flew to the United States. She asked Americans to help Israel. She said, "You cannot decide whether we should fight or not. We will. You can only decide one thing—whether we shall be victorious. I beg of you, don't be too late. The time is now."

American Jews agreed. In just six weeks, Golda raised $50 million.

The money that Golda raised was used to strengthen the Israeli army. Although it was difficult, this army fought off the Arabs. In 1956, Golda became Israel's Foreign Minister. That same year, she changed her last name from Myerson to Meir. In 1969, she became Israel's Prime Minister. She held this post for five years. She kept working to help Israel until her death in 1978.

Directions: Answer questions 4 through 6. You may look back at the story as often as you like.

---

4.   What problems did Golda Meir face and how did she solve them?

■ R<u>OAR</u> — <u>R</u>EAD the question

What does the question ask? _____

_____

■ R<u>O</u>AR — <u>O</u>RGANIZE your thinking

What were the problems and solutions?

Problems   Solutions

■ ROAR — **A**NSWER the question

Write a few paragraphs describing the problems that Golda Meir faced during her lifetime. Use the ideas from your chart for your description.

_____

_____

_____

_____

_____

_____

_____

_____

_____

_____

_____

_____

_____

■ ROAR — **R**EVIEW your answer

- Did you answer the question?   ❏ yes   ❏ no

- Did you make sense?   ❏ yes   ❏ no

- Did you check spelling, capitals, punctuation, language?   ❏ yes   ❏ no

5. Describe what Golda Meir did to help create Israel. Write at least two paragraphs and use examples from the selection.

■ **R**OAR — **R**EAD the question

What does the question ask? _____

_____

■ **RO**AR — **O**RGANIZE your thinking

What steps did Golda take to help create Israel?

FIRST

↓

NEXT

↓

NEXT

↓

NEXT

↓

LAST

■ ROAR — **A**NSWER the question

Use the organizer to help you write your answer. Choose what you think are the most important events that enabled Golda Meir to help create Israel.

_____

_____

_____

_____

_____

_____

_____

_____

_____

_____

_____

_____

■ ROAR — **R**EVIEW your answer

- Did you answer the question?   ❑ yes   ❑ no

- Did you make sense?   ❑ yes   ❑ no

- Did you check spelling, capitals, punctuation, language?   ❑ yes   ❑ no

Directions: This question is about both selections.

6. Write at least three paragraphs showing the similarities and differences you see in the goals the main characters set for themselves.

■ **R**OAR — **R**EAD the question

What does the question ask? _____

_____

■ **R**OAR — **O**RGANIZE your thinking

Complete the Venn Diagram to help you organize your writing.

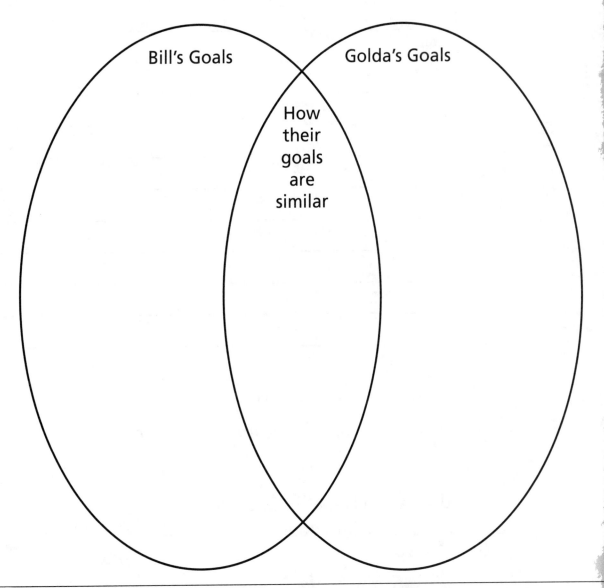

■ ROAR — **A**NSWER the question

Write at least three paragraphs to answer the question. Remember to describe the similarities and differences you see in the goals the main characters had.

_____

_____

_____

_____

_____

_____

_____

_____

_____

_____

_____

_____

_____

_____

_____

_____

_____

■ ROAR — **R**EVIEW your answer

- • Did you answer the question?   ❏ yes   ❏ no

- • Did you make sense?   ❏ yes   ❏ no

- • Did you check spelling, capitals,
  punctuation, language?   ❏ yes   ❏ no

Unit IV

TEST

Now that you have learned the **Get Ready – Read – ROAR** method, you will be able to practice it independently.

In this section you are going to read a story and a poem. You will then be asked to answer some questions about them. Both stories are about the dangers of water.

The **Get Ready – Read – ROAR** Method

Before you read	**Get Ready:** Think about what the selection may be about.
While you read	**Read:** Look for the theme. Think about your predictions.
After you read	**ROAR** Read the question / Organize your thinking / Answer the question / Review your answer

BEFORE YOU BEGIN READING THE TWO SELECTIONS

Before you begin, read the sentences in the box and write a response.

> Some people enjoy the thrill of being on the water. Write about some of the things that might be dangerous.
>
> _____
>
> _____
>
> _____
>
> _____
>
> _____
>
> _____
>
> _____
>
> _____

SELECTION 1

BEFORE YOU READ

In this part, you are going to read a story called *Down a Wild River*. You will be asked to answer some questions about what you have read. Read and answer each question carefully. You can look back at the story as often as you like. Turn to the next page and begin.

Down a Wild River

A spray of water hits you in the face as your raft swirls through the foaming tempest. Someone shouts, "There's a rock ahead!" Quickly, you and your crewmates turn the raft to avoid striking the rock and perhaps tipping over. You are white-water rafting. And it's a thrill!

"White water" is the name given to river rapids. White water forms where a riverbed narrows and drops sharply. There, the water cascades and tumbles down and around rocks. Rafters must know how to move their large rubber boats safely over these rushing waters.

Safety is very important in white-water rafting. Before setting off, everyone puts on a life jacket. Each raft, which may carry between ten and twenty people, has a guide aboard. The guide is a person who knows the river and the rapids. Before departure, the guide gives the crew members important lessons. They learn how to pivot the raft to direct it around rocks, hidden tree trunks, and other dangers. They also learn what to do if a person is thrown out in midstream.

Falling out of a raft in the middle of a river can be a frightening ordeal. Hitting the ice-cold water makes you shiver and gasp for breath. But even scarier is knowing that you will have to fight the rushing waters alone for a while. Not until the raft reaches calmer waters can a lifeline be thrown out. Only then can you be pulled back aboard.

Often a whole raft will turn over. Then the rafters know to head for the shoreline. There, on the bank of the river, they check to make sure that everyone is safe.

A run down a river can take as little as three or four hours. But people who enjoy white-water rafting often take backpacking trips. Hiking by day and camping by night, these nature lovers explore remote areas that are still wild and untouched by civilization.

Directions: Answer the following questions about *Down a Wild River.* Look back at the story as often as you like.

1. What are the dangers involved in white-water rafting? Complete the chart to show the dangers of white-water rafting. Use examples from the story to explain your answer.

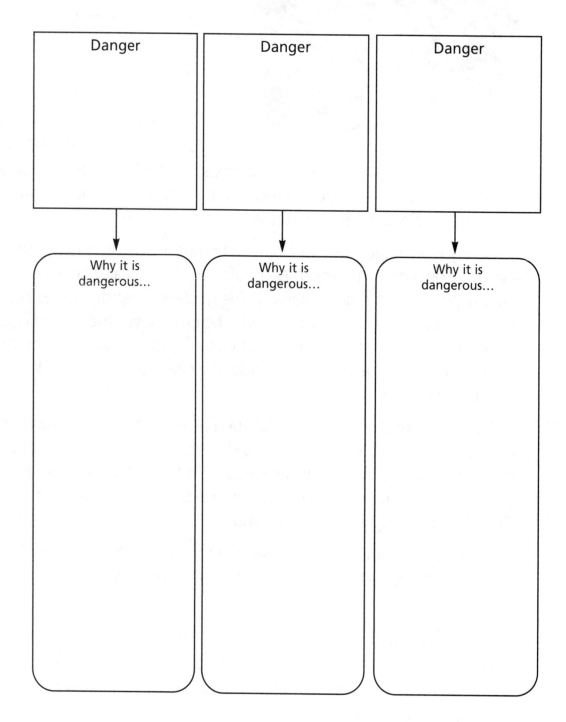

Danger	Danger	Danger
Why it is dangerous...	Why it is dangerous...	Why it is dangerous...

2. How does the guide ensure safety? You may use the space below to create a graphic organizer. Use a list, a web, or a chart. Be sure to give examples from the story.

Create your graphic organizer here.

3. **Who is telling this story, and why does the person think that white-water rafting is a thrill?**

Use this web to organize your writing. Then write three paragraphs that explain who is telling the story and why the person thinks it is a thrill to go white-water rafting. Be sure to give examples from the story.

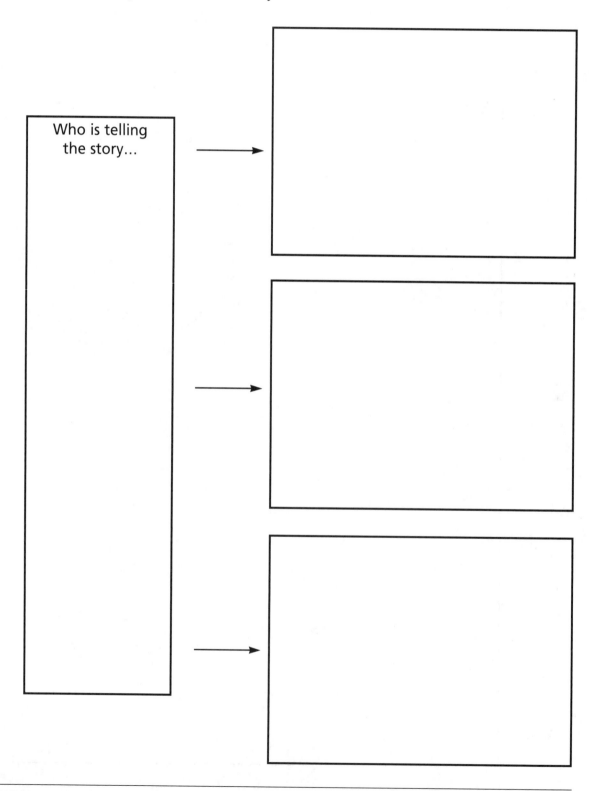

Who is telling
the story...

Write your response here.

_____

_____

_____

_____

_____

_____

_____

_____

_____

_____

_____

_____

_____

_____

_____

_____

_____

_____

_____

_____

_____

_____

_____

_____

_____

In this part, you are going to read the poem *Sea Fever*. It was written by John Masefield. You will then answer some questions about what you have read. Read and answer each question carefully. You can look back at the poem as often as you like.

Sea Fever

I must go down to the seas again,
to the lonely sea and the sky,
And all I ask is a tall ship
and a star to steer her by,
And the wheels kick and the wind's song
and the white sail's shaking,
And a grey mist on the sea's face
and a grey dawn breaking.

I must go down to the seas again,
for the call of the running tide
Is a wild call and a clear call
that may not be denied;
And all I ask is a windy day
with the white clouds flying,
And the flung spray and the blown spume,
and the sea-gulls crying.

I must go down to the seas again,
to the vagrant gypsy life,
To the gull's way and the whale's way
where the wind's like a whetted knife;
And all I ask is a merry yarn
from a laughing fellow-rover,
And quiet sleep and a sweet dream
when the long trick's over.

Directions: Having read the poem, answer questions 4 through 6. You may look back at the story as often as you like.

4.   How does the poet describe a sea voyage?
     Complete the chart. Use examples from the story.

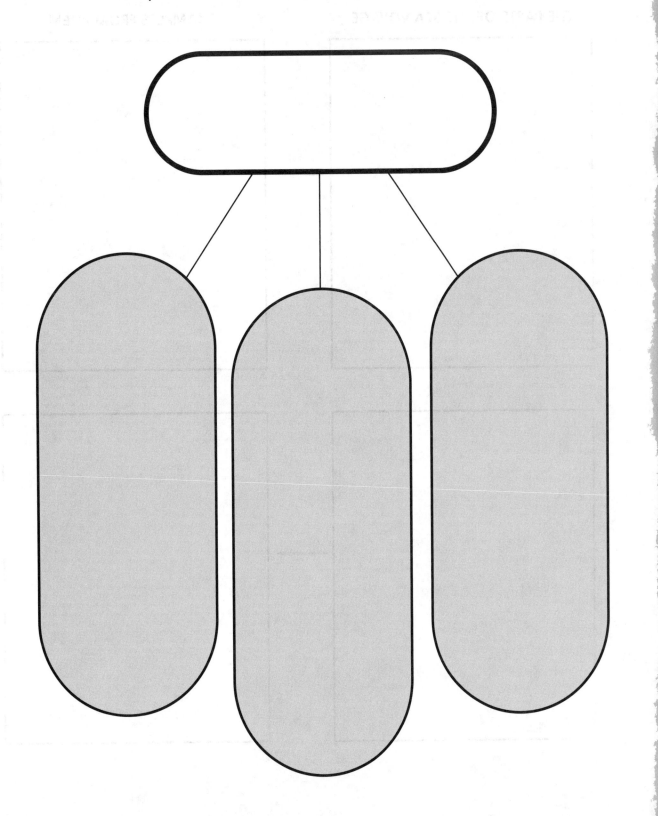

5.   What parts of the sea voyage does the narrator enjoy the most? Complete the chart below. Use examples from the poem to support your answer.

THE PARTS OF THE SEA VOYAGE   **EXAMPLES FROM POEM**

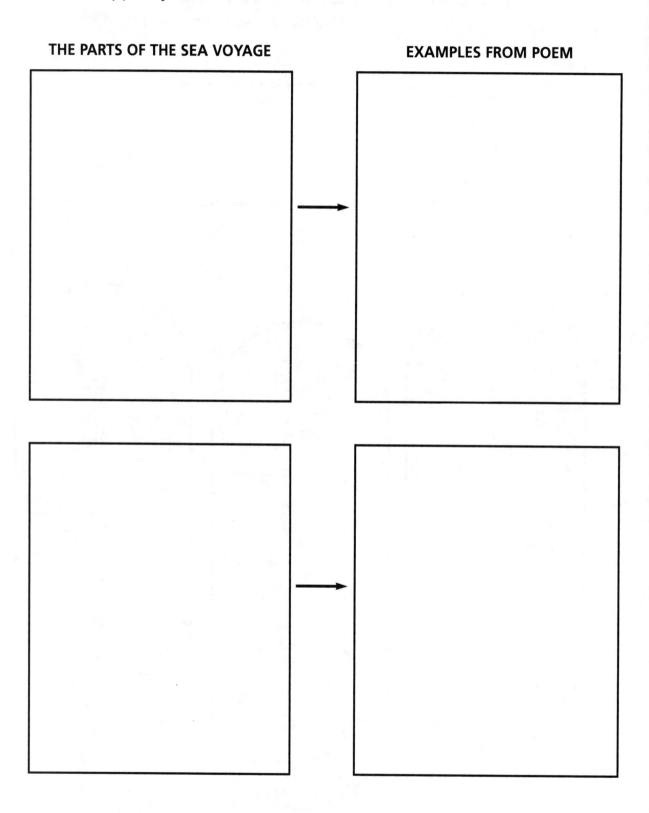

KEYS TO EXCELLENCE IN INTEGRATED LANGUAGE ARTS · LEVEL F

Directions: For this question, remember to think about both selections!

6. Why do characters, in both selections, love the water? First create a graphic organizer. Then write at least two paragraphs explaining your answer using examples from both selections.

Create your graphic organizer here.

Write your response here.

_____

_____

_____

_____

_____

_____

_____

_____

_____

_____

_____

_____

_____

_____

_____

_____

_____

_____

_____

_____

_____

_____

_____

_____

Appendix

GRAPHIC ORGANIZERS

Here is a set of Graphic Organizers. They are the same group of organizers introduced in Unit I and used throughout this text. Use them with your students to provide additional writing opportunities.

Suggestion 1:
- Discuss a topic with your students.
- Direct you students to choose an organizer to help them write their stories.
- Have your students write a story using the information from the organizer they created.

Suggestion 2:
- A student selects an organizer.
- A student creates a piece of writing by first completing the organizer chosen.
- Ask your students why they chose that particular organizer for the type of writing they wrote.

Suggestion 3:
- Provide different types of writing for your students to read and discuss.
- Students choose a style of writing to write their own piece.
- Students use an organizer to assist them in their pre-writing phase. Then they write using the information from the organizer they created.

SEQUENCE MAP

Sequence is the order in which events happen. A **Sequence Map** shows you the order of the events in a story.

```
┌─────────────────────────────────────────────────┐
│ FIRST:                                          │
│                                                 │
│                                                 │
└─────────────────────────────────────────────────┘
                        │
                        ▼
┌─────────────────────────────────────────────────┐
│ FIRST:                                          │
│                                                 │
│                                                 │
└─────────────────────────────────────────────────┘
                        │
                        ▼
┌─────────────────────────────────────────────────┐
│ FIRST:                                          │
│                                                 │
│                                                 │
└─────────────────────────────────────────────────┘
                        │
                        ▼
┌─────────────────────────────────────────────────┐
│ FIRST:                                          │
│                                                 │
│                                                 │
└─────────────────────────────────────────────────┘
                        │
                        ▼
┌─────────────────────────────────────────────────┐
│ FIRST:                                          │
│                                                 │
│                                                 │
└─────────────────────────────────────────────────┘
                        │
                        ▼
┌─────────────────────────────────────────────────┐
│ FIRST:                                          │
│                                                 │
│                                                 │
└─────────────────────────────────────────────────┘
```

STORY MAP

A **Story Map** helps you to understand the parts of a story.

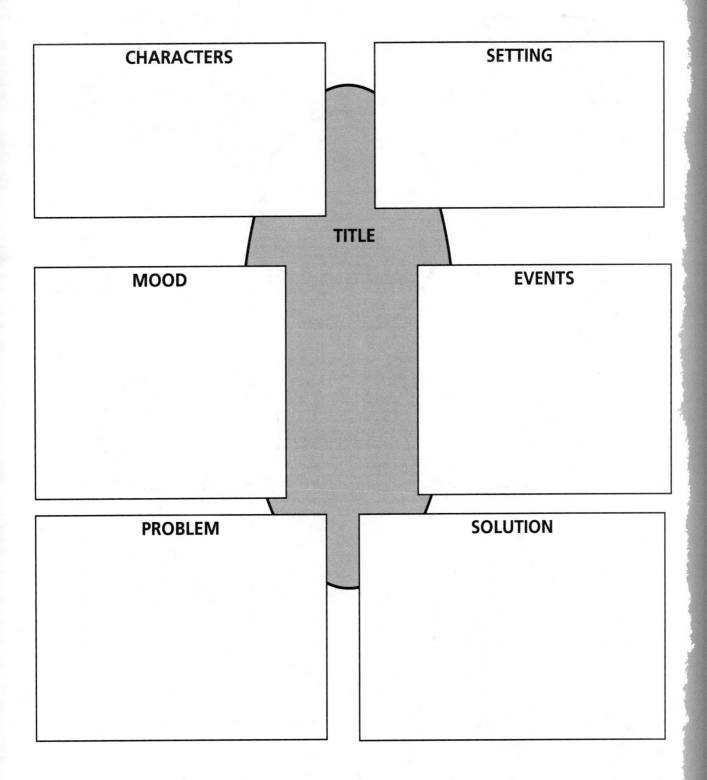

CHARACTERS

SETTING

TITLE

MOOD

EVENTS

PROBLEM

SOLUTION

DESCRIPTIVE MAP I

The **Descriptive Map** will help you describe someone or something.

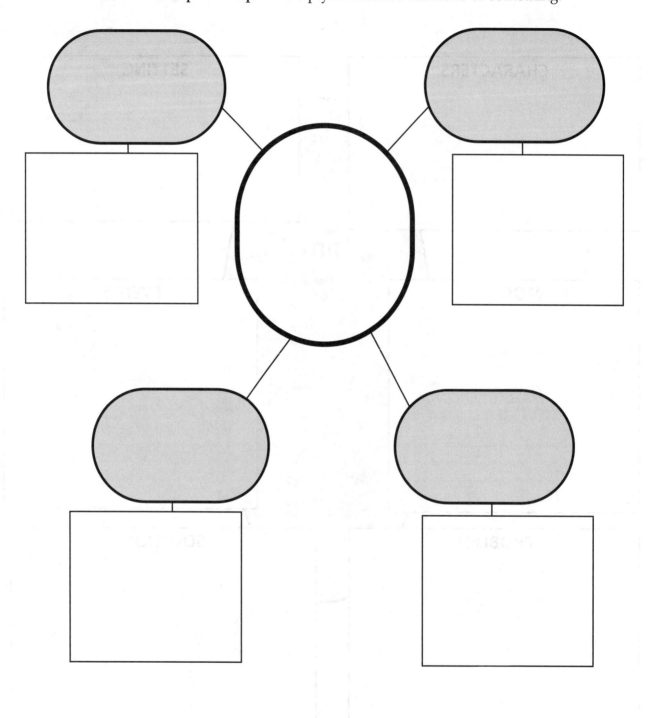

MAIN IDEA MAP

A **Main Idea Map** shows the most important idea and supporting ideas, or subtopics. It also has information about the subtopics.

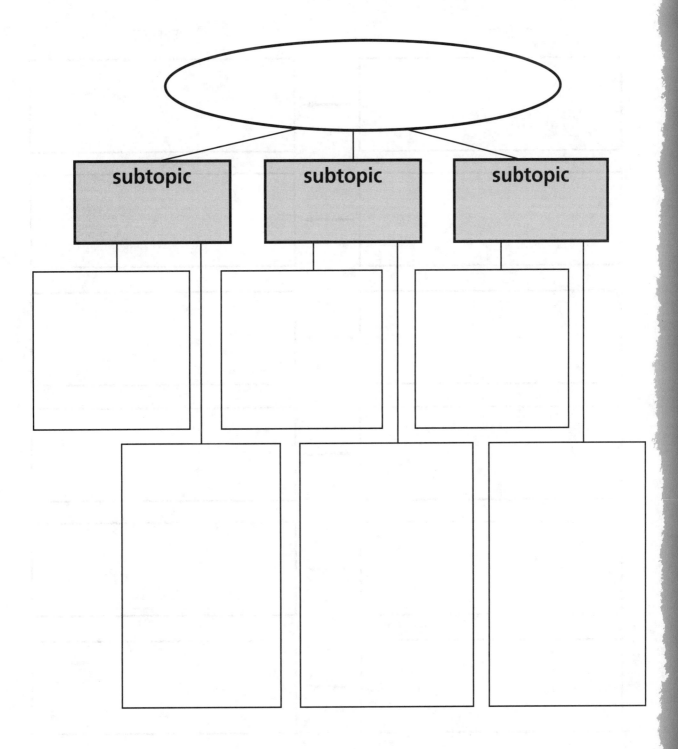

CAUSE AND EFFECT MAP

A **Cause and Effect Map** shows what happened in a story and why it happened. It shows the relationship between events.

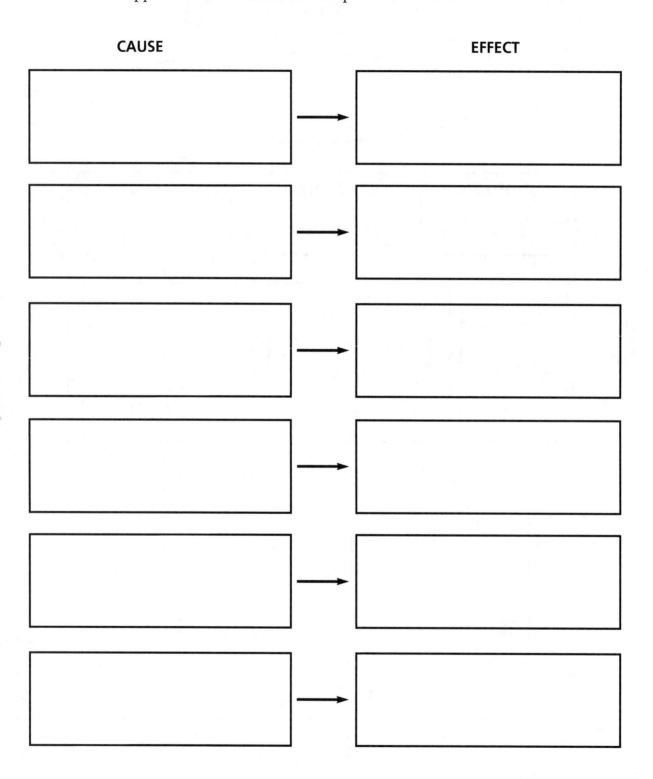

CAUSE   EFFECT

VENN DIAGRAM

A **Venn Diagram** is a picture that shows in what ways two things are alike and not alike.

THEME MAP

A **Theme Map** shows the main topic or subject of a story. It also shows the details that support the theme.

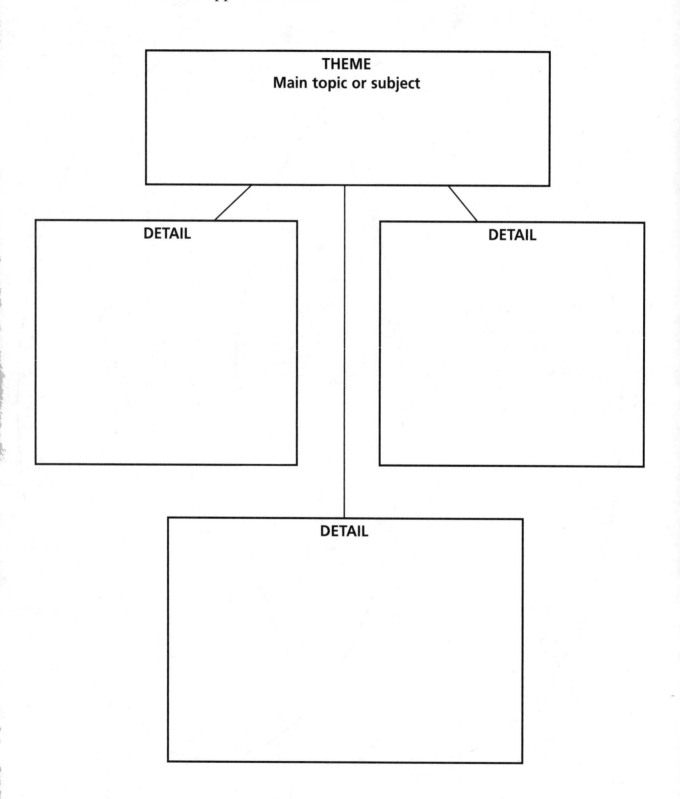

THEME
Main topic or subject

DETAIL

DETAIL

DETAIL